D0334536

Magic Mates

and the Holiday of Horrors

Jane West

Illustrated by
Stik

NORFOLK LIBRARIES & INFORMATION SERVICE	
1272771	
PETERS	09-Oct-2009
JF	£3.99

Rising Stars UK Ltd.
22 Grafton Street, London W1S 4EX
www.risingstars-uk.com

The right of Jane West to be identified as the author of this work has been asserted by her in accordance with the Copyright, Design and Patents Act 1988.

Published 2008

Text, design and layout © Rising Stars UK Ltd.

Cover design: Button plc
Illustrator: Stik, Bill Greenhead for Illustration
Text design and typesetting: Andy Wilson
Publisher: Gill Budgell
Editor: Jane Wood

All rights reserved. No part of this publication may be reproduced, stored in a retrieval system, or transmitted in any form by any means, electronic, mechanical, photocopying, recording or otherwise without the prior permission of Rising Stars UK Ltd.

British Library Cataloguing in Publication Data.
A CIP record for this book is available from the British Library

ISBN: 988 1 84680 338 3

Printed in the UK by CPI Bookmarque, Croydon, CR0 4TD

FSC
Mixed Sources
Product group from well-managed forests and other controlled sources
www.fsc.org Cert no. TT-COC-002227
© 1996 Forest Stewardship Council

Contents

Meet the Magic Mates

The Magic Mates are best friends – but that doesn't mean they're all alike.

The sporty one: can climb trees, surf and take on the boys at their own game – and win.

Travels by: running!

Loves: trendy tracksuits, open skies and sandy beaches.

Hates: standing still.

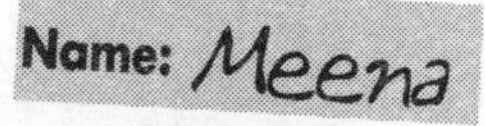

The girly one: uses her mobile for networking and planning her social life.

Travels by: Mum's car (her personal chauffeur).

Loves: pink and her Magic Mates.

Hates: breaking a nail.

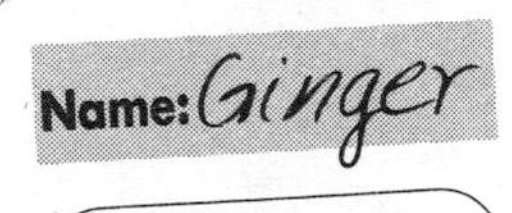

The ginger one: you don't wanna mess with this feisty gal – the Kung Fu and quick quip queen!

Travels by: push-scooter.

Loves: Jackie Chan and her Magic Mate pals.

Hates: nail extensions.

The clever one: uses her brains and quick wit to talk her way out of trouble. Sometimes she's a bit too quick.

Travels by: bicycle and is designing a pair of motorised rollerblades.

Loves: Jacqueline Wilson, Cathy Cassidy and Albert Einstein.

Hates: being called 'geek', 'nerd', 'swot' or 'boffin'.

The fashion-conscious one: can tell her Prada from her Asda and knows how to accessorise.

Travels by: limousine, of course! (But only in her dreams.)

Loves: shopping.

Hates: anything to do with getting dirty; anyone who upsets her Magic Mates.

The funky punky one: the 'alternative' one of the gang who hugs trees, people and furry animals.

Travels by: skateboard.

Loves: having a good time.

Hates: bullies.

The Sun Always Shines

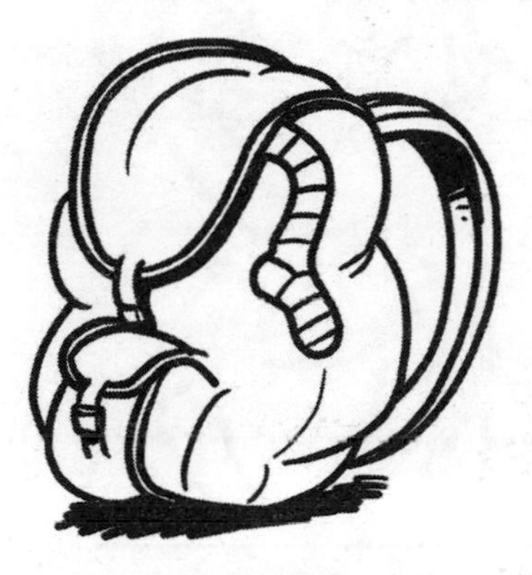

The Magic Mates are off on their holidays. It wasn't easy deciding where to go because they all like doing different things. But Izzie's mum thinks she has the perfect solution – Aunty Viv's caravan by the seaside. It sounds wonderful: sun, sea and sand, and all the Magic Mates together.

Izzie Look! I can see the sea!

Meena And the sun is shining.

Jo We must be nearly there.

Izzie Mum said Aunty Viv
would meet us at the station
and take us to the caravan.

Aunty Viv Hi, Izzie. These must be your friends. Hello, everyone. I can tell you're going to have a good week.

Jo Did the weather on TV show sunshine?

Aunty Viv I haven't got a TV – but I read it in my crystal ball.

Yash Pardon?

Izzie Aunty Viv is … a bit different.

Aunty Viv That's me! Well, who wants to be the same as everyone else?

Ginger Too right!

Ellie Are we going in your van?

Aunty Viv Yes. This way, girls.

Meena At least it's not a broomstick.

The girls climb in the van and soon they're bumping down a country road. The windows are down, and they can smell the sea.

Aunty Viv Here we are, girls.

Meena Oh, it's so beautiful!
Are we staying in that caravan?

Aunty Viv Yes, it's all yours
for a whole week, but my friend,
Mrs Pengelly, is just over there
in the farmhouse. Here's her
phone number, just in case.

Izzie Wow, thanks, Aunty Viv!

Aunty Viv There's a tap outside,
and you can wash in the stream.
It's not too cold. You can get
fresh milk, eggs and bread from
Mrs Pengelly every morning.
And if you leave her a list,
she'll get you some food
from the supermarket, too.
Oh, and you'll find I've put some
chocolate and fruit juice
in the caravan already.

Izzie Thanks, Aunty Viv.
You're the best!

Aunty Viv If you need anything,
just give me a call
or Mrs Pengelly can help you.

Ellie Do you have a telephone?

Aunty Viv Yes, but you can borrow
my crystal ball if you like.

Izzie You're teasing us!

Aunty Viv Just a bit!
Oh, one thing
I should say,
don't go down
to the house beyond the lake –
they're not too keen on visitors.
And don't worry if you hear
any howling. Have a good
holiday, girls!

Ellie I hope she was joking
about the howling!

Meena I hope she was joking about
washing in the stream!

Jo I don't think so. There's no shower in here, just six bunk beds and a little cooker. Er, Meena, I don't know how to tell you this, but the loo is in that shed under the tree.

Meena Outside?

Izzie It's a caravan – everything is outside.

Ginger It'll be fun.

Yash It's an adventure.

Things That Go Bump in the Night

It's the first night and Meena wakes up. It's dark and she can hear rain on the caravan roof. Worse still, her sleeping bag is getting wet. The caravan is leaking.

Meena Oh no! I'm being rained on! It's making me want to go to the loo. I don't want to go out to that horrid shed in the rain by myself.

Izzie Meena! You woke me up. What's the matter?

Meena I hate it here! The loo is outside, there's no shower, the field has turned into a bog and now I'm getting rained on in bed! If we stay here any longer, they'll need to rescue us by boat!

Izzie I'll phone Mrs Pengelly. She'll come and get us. At least her house should be dry.

Izzie picks up her mobile phone.
But there's a problem.

Izzie Oh no!

Meena What now?

Izzie I can't get a signal. We'll have to go to Mrs Pengelly's house.

Meena I'll come with you.

Izzie You'll get soaked.

Meena I'm already soaked but I'm not letting you go off in the dark by yourself. I'll write a note to let the others know where we've gone in case they wake up.

The girls pull on some shoes and coats and head off to the farmhouse carrying torches. It's hard to see with the rain blowing in their faces. Soon they are lost.

Meena	Where's the farmhouse?
Izzie	I don't know. We must have missed it in the dark.
Meena	But that's impossible.
Izzie	If we walk up the hill, we might be able to see it.

The girls are cold and wet and fed up. It doesn't look like it can get any worse – but it can. They jump when they hear something howling.

Meena Aaaaaaaaaagh!

Izzie What was that?

Out of the Frying Pan ...

Meena and Izzie have been scared by something howling. It sounds big. And it sounds like it's close.

Meena I'm scared!

Izzie Me too. At least the rain has stopped.

Meena Yes, 'cos it really helps to see what's about to eat you!

Izzie We're not going to be eaten. There haven't been any wild wolves in Britain for ages.

Meena What about bears?

Izzie There aren't any bears either.

Meena What about lions?

Izzie Sssh. I heard something.

A loud howl echoes across the fields.

Meena Can we run now?

Izzie Yes! This way!

The girls run as fast as they can. Suddenly Izzie stops and Meena almost bumps into her.

Meena Why have you stopped running?

Izzie I've got a signal on my phone!

Meena Thank goodness!

Izzie Mrs Pengelly, it's Izzie.
The caravan is leaking,
everything is wet and we're lost!
Can you come and get us?

Mrs P Oh dear. I'll come out
to find you. I'm so glad
your phone works – you can't
always get a signal
in the caravan.

Izzie We had to go outside.

Mrs P Do you know where you are?

Izzie Er … not exactly.
We thought we knew how
to get to your house,
but we got lost.

Mrs P What can you see, Izzie?

Izzie Not a lot. Oh, hang on.
There's a big house near
a lake …

Mrs P No, no, NO!
Don't move, I'll …

Izzie Oh no! Stupid phone.
Don't cut out again now!

But it's too late. A huge wolf
is grinning at them.
And it has very sharp teeth.

Meena You're good with animals.
Talk to it.

Izzie I'm good with animals,
not monsters. Er ... good boy.
Sit. Stay ... I don't think
it's working.

… And Into the Fire!

The girls are really scared.
The monster wolf is coming closer.

Meena Let's run for it!

Izzie No, that's the worst thing you can do. He would think you're afraid.

Meena He'd be right!

The wolf's eyes glow yellow in the moonlight. Izzie thinks that screaming might be a good idea. Meena is thinking about fainting. Then they hear a voice.

Mrs P Down, Grizzly. Leave those poor girls alone. Girls, don't be scared of the wolf. He won't hurt you. He's just being nosey.

Meena Izzie, I told you I heard a wolf.
You said there weren't
any wild wolves!

Mrs P Grizzly isn't a wild wolf.
He lives at the animal centre
by the lake, but he gets out
sometimes.

Izzie So that was why Aunty Viv told us to keep away from here.

Mrs P Yes, because Grizzly gets scared if there are too many people around. There aren't any wild wolves left in Britain. Even if there were, they'd be more afraid of you.

Meena I'm not sure about that!

Izzie Why do you call him 'Grizzly'? It makes him sound scary.

Mrs P It's supposed to be a joke, because Grizzly is really a bit of a scaredy cat.

Izzie You might want to work on your jokes, Mrs Pengelly!

Mrs P I'm just not sure how you got here when you were trying to find my house.

Izzie We got in a bit of a muddle when the caravan started leaking. You are closer than Aunty Viv, so we tried to phone you. We had to go outside. Then I lost the signal on my mobile. We just got lost in the dark.

Mrs P My house is just beyond the trees, there, look. Let's go and get dry.

The girls arrive at Mrs Pengelly's.
As they sit by the fire in the warm kitchen toasting marshmallows, their adventure doesn't seem so scary.

Mrs Pengelly
Oh, you poor dears!
You've had quite an adventure.
I bet that silly Grizzly gave you a scare.

Izzie You could say that!

Meena It was really scary when we heard him howling.

Mrs P What do you mean?
Grizzly doesn't howl.
He never has.

Izzie Well, there was something howling out there – and it wasn't just Meena!

Mrs P Oh, I'm sure you imagined it.
More tea, dears?

Meena and Izzie look at each other. They are both thinking the same thing. It's time to call Aunty Viv to rescue all the Magic Mates and take them to her cottage by the sea. Now *that* sounds more like a holiday from heaven rather than a holiday of horrors!

About the Author

Jane West has never had a holiday quite like that one, but she knows how spooked you can get if you sit round a camp fire and swap ghost stories or horror stories …

Jane West:

 lives by the beach in Cornwall

 likes taking her dog Pip paddling in the sea

 loves bodyboarding

 has worked in an art gallery, a bookshop and a school.

Now she's a writer, and has had great fun writing about the Magic Mates. She hopes you liked reading about them.

Wolf Facts

 *Dogs and wolves are closely related.*

Wolves come in many shapes, sizes and colours. Some wolves are white (the ones who live in snowy areas); others are brown, grey or black.

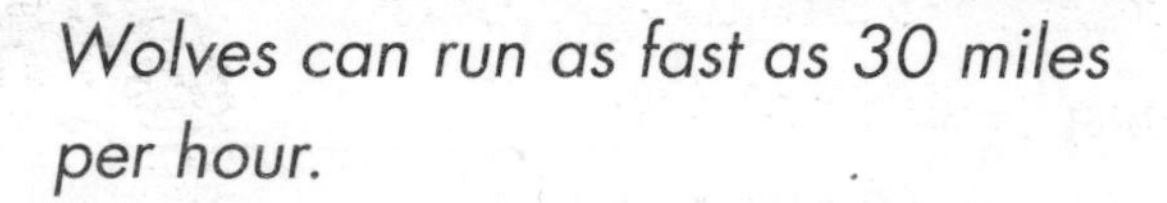

Wolves can run as fast as 30 miles per hour.

 Wolf cubs are born with blue eyes. Their eyes turn yellowy-orange as the cubs grow up.

 *A wolf's sense of smell is 100 times better than a human's.*

- *Wolves howl to greet one another.*
- Wolves are good swimmers.
- *The last wild wolf in the UK lived over 250 years ago.*
- Wolves are related to dogs, but they're not dogs. You can't have a wolf as a pet.

If you want to find out more wolf facts, go to: **www.everythingwolf.com** or **www.wolftrust.org.uk**.

Wolf Lingo

cub	baby wolf
howl	how wolves 'talk' over long distances
pack	the wolf's family and friends
prey	what a wolf eats: usually smaller animals such as rabbits
lone wolf	an outcast wolf who lives by itself, like Grizzly. A lone wolf rarely howls.

Not All Wolves Are Baddies!

Do you know
the ancient legend
about the twin boys,
Romulus and Remus?

Some say that their dad was Mars,
the Roman god of War!

The two baby boys were left by themselves
in a forest. They were found by a wolf
who felt sorry for them. She fed them with her
own milk and looked after them. The boys
grew up into strong men.

One day, the brothers had a big fight
and Remus was killed. After this, Romulus
founded a new city. It became the capital city
of Italy and was named after him: Rome.

Nobody knows if that story is true,
but at least the wolf in it was a goodie!

Izzie's Favourite Wolf Jokes

How do wolves eat?
They wolf it down!
What do you get when you cross a wolf with a glove?
I don't know, but I wouldn't want to shake hands with it.

Wolf Quiz

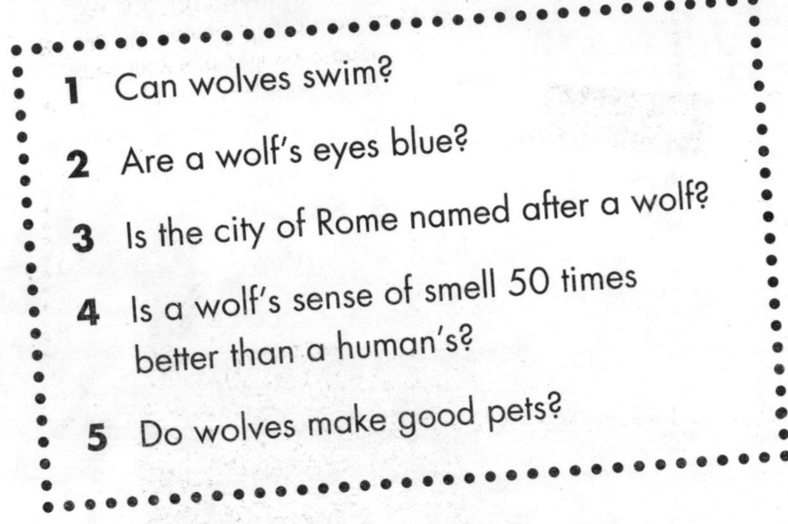

1. Can wolves swim?
2. Are a wolf's eyes blue?
3. Is the city of Rome named after a wolf?
4. Is a wolf's sense of smell 50 times better than a human's?
5. Do wolves make good pets?

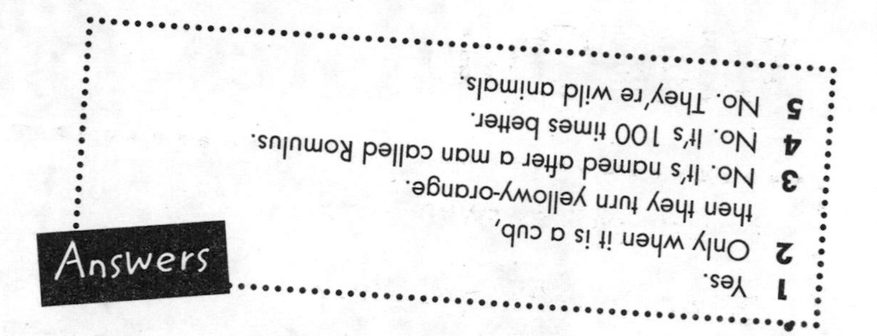

How did you score?

0–1 You must be a lone wolf!

2–3 You're not a member of the pack yet.

4–5 You're the leader of the pack!

RISING STARS

Magic Mates books are available from most booksellers.

For mail order information
please call Rising Stars on 0871 47 23 010
or visit www.risingstars-uk.com